熄灯时间到！

【美】露西·瑞切·潘纳◎著
【美】杰瑞·史麦斯◎绘
范晓星◎译

天津出版传媒集团

新蕾出版社

献给艾美莉亚·哥特纳。

——露西·瑞切·潘纳

献给罗伯塔·普莱塞尔。

——杰瑞·史麦斯

图书在版编目 (CIP) 数据

熄灯时间到！ /（美）潘纳（Penner,L.R.）著；（美）史麦斯（Smath,J.）绘；范晓星译.
—天津：新蕾出版社，2014.1（2024.12 重印）

（数学帮帮忙·互动版）

书名原文：Lights Out!

ISBN 978-7-5307-5901-1

Ⅰ.①熄…

Ⅱ.①潘…②史…③范…

Ⅲ.①数学–儿童读物

Ⅳ.①O1–49

中国版本图书馆 CIP 数据核字(2013)第 270437 号

Lights Out! by Lucille Recht Penner;
Illustrated by Jerry Smath.

Copyright © 2000 by Kane Press, Inc.

All rights reserved, including the right of reproduction in whole or in part in any form. This edition published by arrangement with Kane Press, Inc. New York, NY, represented by Lerner Publishing Group through The ChoiceMaker Korea Co. Agency.

Simplified Chinese translation copyright © 2014 by New Buds Publishing House (Tianjin) Limited Company

ALL RIGHTS RESERVED

本书中文简体版专有出版权经由中华版权代理中心授予新蕾出版社（天津）有限公司。未经许可，不得以任何方式复制或抄袭本书的任何部分。

津图登字：02–2012–226

出版发行：天津出版传媒集团
新蕾出版社

http://www.newbuds.com.cn

地　　址：天津市和平区西康路 35 号(300051)
出 版 人：马玉秀
电　　话：总编办 (022)23332422
　　　　　发行部 (022)23332679　23332351
传　　真：(022)23332422
经　　销：全国新华书店
印　　刷：天津新华印务有限公司
开　　本：787mm×1092mm　1/16
印　　张：3
版　　次：2014 年 1 月第 1 版　2024 年 12 月第 24 次印刷
定　　价：12.00 元

无处不在的数学

资深编辑　卢　江

人们常说"兴趣是最好的老师"，有了兴趣，学习就会变得轻松愉快。数学对于孩子来说或许有些难，因为比起语文，数学显得枯燥、抽象，不容易理解，孩子往往不那么喜欢。可许多家长都知道，学数学对于孩子的成长和今后的生活有多么重要。不仅数学知识很有用，学习数学过程中获得的数学思想和方法更会影响孩子的一生，因为数学素养是构成人基本素质的一个重要因素。但是，怎样才能让孩子对数学产生兴趣呢？怎样才能激发他们兴致勃勃地去探索数学问题呢？我认为，让孩子读些有趣的书或许是不错的选择。读了这套"数学帮帮忙"，我立刻产生了想把它们推荐给教师和家长朋友们的愿望，因为这真是一套会让孩子爱上数学的好书！

这套有趣的图书从美国引进，原出版者是美国资深教育专家。每本书讲述一个孩子们生活中的故事，由故事中出现的问题自然地引入一个数学知识，然后通过运用数学知识解决问题。比如，从帮助外婆整理散落的纽扣引出分类，从为小狗记录藏骨头的地点引出空间方位等等。故事素材全部来源于孩子们的真实生活,不是童话,不是幻想,而是鲜活的生活实例。正是这些发生在孩子身边的故事,让孩子们懂得,数学无处不在并且非常有用;这些鲜活的实例也使得抽象的概念更易于理解,更容易激发孩子学习数学的兴趣,让他们逐渐爱上数学。这样的教育思想和方法与我国近年来提倡的数学教育理念是十分吻合的!

这是一套适合5~8岁孩子阅读的书,书中的有趣情节和生动的插画可以将抽象的数学问题直观化、形象化,为孩子的思维活动提供具体形象的支持。如果亲子共读的话,家长可以带领孩子推测情节的发展,探讨解决难题的办法,让孩子在愉悦的氛围中学到知识和方法。

值得教师和家长朋友们注意的是,在每本书的后面,出版者还加入了"互动课堂"及"互动练习",一方面通过一些精心设计的活动让孩子巩固新学到的数学知识,进一步体会知识的含义和实际应用;另一方面帮助家长指导孩子阅读,体会故事中数学之外的道理,逐步提升孩子的阅读理解能力。

我相信孩子读过这套书后一定会明白,原来,数学不是烦恼,不是包袱,数学真能帮大忙!

我是家里最小的孩子。
我总是得第一个去睡觉。
哥哥可以 10 点睡觉。
姐姐可以 9 点睡觉。
你们猜，我几点就得去睡觉？
8 点！这公平吗？

3

每天晚上都是如此。我关了灯，上了床，望向窗外。

街对面是一幢公寓大楼，几乎每家的灯都还亮着，只有我必须睡觉了。

这怎么可能公平？

今晚，我把所有亮灯的人家数了一遍，总共 32 家，32！

这么多人都还没睡呢！

我跑进客厅。"我总是世界上第一个关灯睡觉的人。"我说,"今天晚上,我想做最后一个。求你们啦。明天不用上学。"

妈妈说:"那好吧。"爸爸也同意了。"你可以亮着灯。"他们对我说,"就这一次哟!"

太好啦!今晚一定棒极了!

　　我又把亮灯的人家数了一遍。刚才还亮着32盏灯，现在只有30盏了。2户人家已经睡觉了。

　　我可不睡！

　　我在本子上写下 30。开局不错！等我从窗
户看到所有人家都熄灯了，我才睡呢。到那
时，世界上其他的人可能也都睡着了吧。哈！

一楼有个女孩关上了灯。

过了一分钟，二楼有2盏灯熄灭了。

接着又是1盏。有4盏灯熄灭了。

我在本子上写下 30-4。很简单,我倒着数得到了答案,还剩下 26 盏灯!

我看看表。9 点了。我已经比平时晚睡了一个小时。

可我一点儿都不困!

　　一位女士走进房间，在她的鹦鹉笼子上盖上布罩，然后关上了灯。又熄了 2 盏灯？不对不对，我不能把鹦鹉也算上呀，只熄了 1 盏灯，还有 25 盏灯亮着。

透过一扇窗户我看到一对双胞胎兄弟。他们在玩枕头大战。他们的妈妈走进房间。

兄弟俩跳上了床。这位妈妈亲亲他们，然后关上灯。她把自己卧室的灯也关上了。接着，同一楼层又熄灭了2盏灯。这样又熄了4盏灯。还有21盏灯亮着！

人们真是早早儿就犯困了啊。我也有
些困了。可我有办法让自己不困！我放上
音乐，跳起舞来。

　　突然，有6盏灯熄灭了！我抓过本子。这
一回，我得用退位减法算出答案：21－6＝15！

一位男士在窗前做跳跃运动，看起来很好玩儿。我也做了几下。他关上了灯。他这层的所有人家都熄灯了。

哇！那层的所有人家总是同时去睡觉吗？那层有 8 盏灯。15−8=7。还有 7 户人家亮着灯，而我会是那个坚持到最后的人。我已经等不及啦！

这是怎么回事？有个男孩关上了灯，却又打开手电筒看起书来。他读啊读啊。那本书一定很好看。

"要是你不关上手电筒的话，我就不能把你算上。"我自言自语，"明天再看完这本书吧！"

你想不到吧？那个男孩果真关上了手电筒。7-1=6。

　　对面的灯光变得模糊起来，我肯定是把眼睛闭上了一秒钟。等我再睁大眼睛一看，突然又有3盏灯熄灭了。

　　现在只有3盏灯还亮着。

　　我已经困得受不了了。我打了个一分钟的小
盹儿。等我猛地睁开眼睛时,好啊!现在只有 2 盏
灯亮着。我打盹儿时,一定又熄了 1 盏灯。

做最后一个睡觉的人真难。可我能做到！

我扮起好玩儿的鬼脸让自己保持清醒：先扮一个恐龙，真够吓人的！再扮一个笑笑犬，真不白折腾，又1盏灯熄灭了！

现在,只有1盏灯还亮着! 为什么还不关灯呀? 那家人不知道有多晚了吗? 他们那边出什么事了吗?

　　我觉得累极了。我闭上眼睛，就歇一分钟。但我没睡，绝对没有。我还在跟那个不睡觉的家伙比赛呢。我就要赢了。可我实在太累了。我得在床上躺一下，就……一……秒……钟……

等我睁开眼睛，太阳高照。已经是早晨了！真不公平。我昨天那么努力，可还是没有成为最后睡觉的那个人。

我看着昨晚最后还亮着灯的那扇窗户。窗帘拉上去了。屋里有一个戴红色棒球帽的男孩。

我认识那个男孩，他叫丹尼尔，和我一样大，我们在同一所学校上学。他怎么能那么晚还不睡觉呢？

我和妈妈走到游乐场。我看到丹尼尔从拐角处走过来。"这个男生，昨晚你熬夜了。"我说，"我自己睡得就很晚，但我看到你家灯还亮着。"

　　"哦。"丹尼尔说，"我睡觉总是开着灯，都是因为我弟弟。他是个小宝宝嘛！不过开着灯我也睡得很香。昨晚我8点钟就睡着了。"

29

　　太棒啦！我觉得真开心。这下绝对公平了！昨晚我是最后一个睡觉的人，也许还是全世界最后一个睡的呢！

可我必须承认,我真的太累了,真的。今晚,我迫不及待地想早早儿上床睡觉!

减　法

这里有几种做减法的方法：

1. 倒着数　　　　$15-8=?$

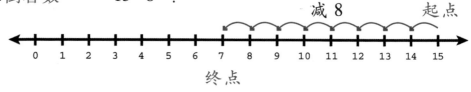

2. 用加法联想　　　　　　　　　　$9-3=?$

我知道 $6+3=9$，所以 $9-3=6$。

3. 5 个 5 个地倒着数

20,15,10,5

4. 找规律

$$40-10=30 \qquad 60-10=50 \qquad 80-10=70$$
$$60-30=30 \qquad 70-30=40 \qquad 90-20=70$$

5. 两位数减法

先减个位，再减十位。

		3 11	7 10
54	35	A̶1̶	8̶0̶
-12	$-\ 4$	-26	$-\ 7$
42	31	15	73

不用退位　　　　　　　　　从十位借十，然后退位再做减法。

32

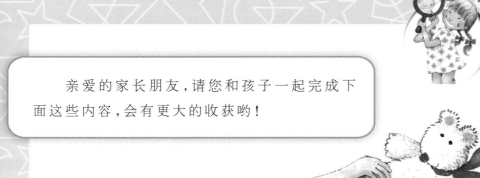

亲爱的家长朋友,请您和孩子一起完成下面这些内容,会有更大的收获哟!

提高阅读能力

• 请孩子看看封面,问问他,人们一般在什么时候会说"熄灯啦"?让孩子说一说,为什么我们要保证充足的睡眠时间?

• 读过第 3 页后,请孩子注意"我"这个字。问问孩子,是谁在讲故事?请孩子在书中指出小主人公。

• 在第 20~21 页,有一个打着手电筒看书的男孩。告诉孩子为什么这样做会伤害眼睛。

互动课堂

巩固数学概念

- 和孩子一边读故事一边验算书里的减法是否正确。算一算,对面大楼最后一共熄灭了多少盏灯?
- 用故事情节编一些减法题。比如,故事里的小主人公比她的哥哥多睡几个小时?比她姐姐呢?
- 锻炼孩子的读图能力。比如,请孩子描述出每层楼有几盏灯亮着,几盏灯熄灭了。
- 请看第 32 页,问问孩子,故事里的小主人公用了哪些方法做减法?

生活中的数学

参考第 32 页,让孩子用零钱来玩减法。

- 蓓蓓有 9 分钱。她把 3 分钱给了别人,她还有几分钱?
- 阿特想有 4 毛钱,可他只有 2 毛钱。他还差多少钱?
- 沙尔有 3 毛 2 分钱。露露有 1 毛 5 分钱。谁的钱多?多多少?

玩骰子

　　每个骰子相对的两个面的点数加起来都等于7。

　　你能猜出这个骰子看不到的那些面上的点数是几吗？

　　让我想想，　　这面是3,那么它的对面就是7-3……

$$
\begin{matrix}
7 \\
\diagup \diagdown \\
3 \quad ?
\end{matrix}
\rightarrow
\begin{matrix}
7 \\
\diagup \diagdown \\
3 \quad 4
\end{matrix}
$$
啊，对面是4!

你也试试！

连连看

算一算,把答案按从小到大的顺序连起来。
现在你知道连出来的是什么图案了吗?

5－2

8－6

9－4

7－3

4－3

20－10

7－1

8－0

10－3

10－1

插花能手

你知道每个花瓶里少几枝花吗?
请按花瓶上的提示数字,把缺少的花画上去吧! 试试看!

需要 11 枝花,已经有 6 枝了,还少几枝?11-6 该怎么算呢?

11-6我是这样想的

先算 10-6=4
再算 4+1=5
所以 11-6=5

$$\begin{array}{r} 11 \\ -\ 6 \\ \hline 5 \end{array}$$

糖果屋

总花费	每人两种糖	
9 元	水果糖	
7 元		奶 糖
13 元	棒棒糖	
11 元		橡皮糖

你知道他们各买了哪两种糖吗？

水果糖 2 元	草莓巧克力 8 元
白巧克力 7 元	橡皮糖 4 元
奶糖 3 元	棒棒糖 5 元

找车位

为小汽车找到数目相同的车位吧！注意不是每辆车都有位置哟！

10 − 2

15 − 5

12 − 3

9 − 4

18 − 12

17 − 6

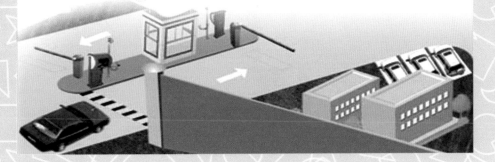

比一比

比一比，算一算，哪边的得数大，请在圆圈里打"✓"。

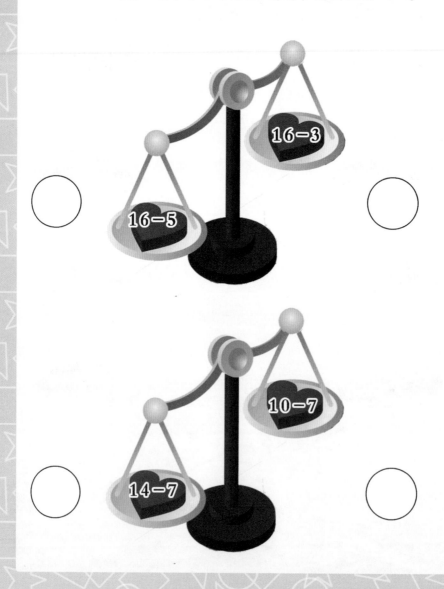

谁转到的结果最大，就可以得到大
奖！我要转到哪个颜色才能得大奖呢？

互动练习1:3 对 4,5 对 2,6 对 1

互动练习2:

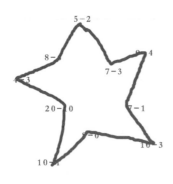

互动练习5:

互动练习3:

分别少5枝、7枝、5枝、10枝。

互动练习4:

	9 元	水果糖	白巧克力
	7 元	橡皮糖	奶　糖
	13 元	棒棒糖	草莓巧克力
	11 元	白巧克力	橡皮糖

互动练习6:

互动练习7:红色

(习题设计:骆　双)

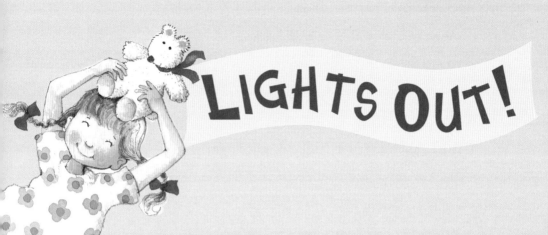

LIGHTS OUT!

I'm the youngest kid in my family.

I have to go to sleep before everyone else.

My brother goes to sleep at 10 o'clock.

My sister can stay up until 9:00.

Guess when I have to go to sleep? 8 o'clock. Is that fair?

Every night is the same. I turn out my light and get into bed. I look out the window.

There is a big apartment building across the street. Almost every light is on—and I have to go to bed.

How can this be fair?

Tonight I count the lights. There are 32 of them. 32!

All those people are still up!

I march into the living room. "I am always the first person in the world to put my light out," I say. "Tonight I want to be the last person to do it. Please let me. There's no school tomorrow."

My mother says, "Okay." My father does too. "You can keep the light on," they tell me. "Just this once."

FANtastic. This will be a great night.

I count the lights again. There were 32 lights before. Now there are only 30. Two people are already asleep.

Not me!

I write 30 in my notebook. A good start. I'm going to stay up until every light I see from my window is out. By then everyone else in the world will probably be asleep. Ha!

A girl on the first floor turns out her light.

A minute later 2 lights go out on the second floor.

Then another. That's 4 lights.

I write 30 minus 4 in my notebook. This is easy. I count back to get the answer. There are 26 lights to go!

I look at my clock. It says 9 o'clock. I've already stayed up one hour longer than I usually do.

And I'm not a bit sleepy.

A woman comes into a room and covers her parrot's cage with a cloth. Then she turns out her light. Is that 2 more? No. I can't count the parrot. It's only 1 light. There are 25 lights left.

In one window I see twin boys. They are having a pillow fight. Their mother comes into the room.

The boys jump into bed. She kisses them and turns out the light. She turns out her light, too. Then 2 more lights go off on the same floor. That's 4 more lights out. 21 still to go!

People sure get sleepy early. I'm a little sleepy myself. I have an idea to wake myself up. I'll put on some music and dance.

All of a sudden 6 lights go out! I grab my notebook. Now I have to regroup to get the answer. 21 minus 6 is 15!

A man is doing jumping jacks at his window. It looks like fun. I do a few, too. The man turns out his light. All the other lights on his floor go out.

Wow! Do the people on that floor always go to sleep at the same time? There were 8 lights on that floor. 15 minus 8 is 7. Seven lights to go and I will be the last one up. I can hardly wait.

Now what? A boy turns out his light, but he starts reading with a flashlight. He reads and reads. That book must be terrific.

"I can't count you if your flashlight is on," I think. "Finish the book tomorrow."

What do you know? The boy turns out the flashlight. 7 minus 1 is 6.

The lights are getting blurry. I must have closed my eyes for a second. I open them very wide and suddenly 3 lights go out.

Now only 3 lights are still on.

I'm very sleepy. I doze for a minute. Then my eyes snap open. Great! Only 2 lights are on now. A light must have gone out while I had my eyes closed.

It's hard to be the last one up. But I can do it.

I make funny faces to keep myself awake. I make my dinosaur face. It's awesome! Then I make my laughing hyena face. And I get my reward. A light goes out!

Now there's only 1 light left! Why doesn't it go out? Doesn't that person know how late it is? What's going on over there?

I'm very tired. I close my eyes for just one minute. But I'm not asleep. Definitely not. This is a contest between me and the other person who isn't asleep. And I am going to win. Except I'm so tired. I need to lie down on my bed for...one...second...

When I open my eyes, the sun is shining. It's morning! This is not fair. I wasn't the last one up even though I tried so hard.

I look at the window that had the last light. The shade flies up. There is a boy with a red baseball hat.

I know that boy. He goes to my school. His name is Daniel and he's my age. How could he stay up so late?

Mom and I walk to the playground. I see Daniel coming around the corner. "Boy, you stay up late," I say. "I was up late myself last night. I saw your light."

"Oh," Daniel says, "I always sleep with my light on because of my little brother. He's such a baby! But the light doesn't bother me. I was asleep by 8:00 last night."

Yipppeeee! I feel great. This is fairer than fair! I was the last person up last night. I was probably the last person up in the whole world!

But I have to admit I'm really, really tired. I can't wait to go to bed tonight!